THE CONCISE
BOB MARLEY

THE CONCISE
BOB MARLEY

WISE PUBLICATIONS
LONDON/NEW YORK/PARIS/SYDNEY/COPENHAGEN/MADRID

EXCLUSIVE DISTRIBUTORS:
MUSIC SALES LIMITED
8/9 FRITH STREET,
LONDON W1V 5TZ, ENGLAND.
MUSIC SALES PTY LIMITED
120 ROTHSCHILD AVENUE,
ROSEBERY, NSW 2018,
AUSTRALIA.

ORDER NO. AM932030
ISBN 0-7119-5199-3
THIS BOOK © COPYRIGHT 1996 BY WISE PUBLICATIONS

COMPILED BY PETER EVANS
MUSIC ARRANGED AND PROCESSED BY BARNES MUSIC ENGRAVING
BOOK DESIGN BY PEARCE MARCHBANK, STUDIO TWENTY, LONDON
PHOTOGRAPHS COURTESY OF LONDON FEATURES INTERNATIONAL

PRINTED IN THE UNITED KINGDOM BY
PAGE BROS., NORWICH, NORFOLK.

YOUR GUARANTEE OF QUALITY.
AS PUBLISHERS, WE STRIVE TO PRODUCE EVERY BOOK TO THE
HIGHEST COMMERCIAL STANDARDS.
THE MUSIC HAS BEEN FRESHLY ENGRAVED AND THE BOOK HAS BEEN CAREFULLY DESIGNED
TO MINIMISE AWKWARD PAGE TURNS AND TO MAKE PLAYING FROM IT A REAL PLEASURE.
THROUGHOUT, THE PRINTING AND BINDING HAVE BEEN PLANNED TO ENSURE A STURDY,
ATTRACTIVE PUBLICATION WHICH SHOULD GIVE YEARS OF ENJOYMENT.
IF YOUR COPY FAILS TO MEET OUR HIGH STANDARDS, PLEASE INFORM US
AND WE WILL GLADLY REPLACE IT.

MUSIC SALES' COMPLETE CATALOGUE DESCRIBES THOUSANDS OF TITLES
AND IS AVAILABLE IN FULL COLOUR SECTIONS BY SUBJECT,
DIRECT FROM MUSIC SALES LIMITED.
PLEASE STATE YOUR AREAS OF INTEREST AND SEND
A CHEQUE/POSTAL ORDER FOR £1.50 FOR POSTAGE TO:
MUSIC SALES LIMITED, NEWMARKET ROAD,
BURY ST. EDMUNDS, SUFFOLK IP33 3YB.

VISIT THE INTERNET MUSIC SHOP AT
http://www.musicsales.co.uk

IN BOTH 'THE LYRICS' AND 'THE MUSIC' SECTIONS
EACH SONG BEARS THE SAME NUMBER, AS LISTED BELOW...

THE LYRICS

1
AFRICA UNITE

Africa unite, 'cause we're moving right out of Babylon,
And we're going to our father's land.

How good and how pleasant it would be,
Before God and man, yeah,
To see the unification of all Africans, yeah.
As it's been said already,
Let it be done, yeah.
We are the children of the Rastaman.
We are the children of the higher man.

Africa unite, 'cause the children wanna come home,
    yeah, yeah, yeah,
Africa unite, 'cause we're moving right out of Babylon
And we're grooving to our father's land.

How good and pleasant it would be,
Before God and man,
To see the unification of all Rastaman, yeah.
As it's been said already,
Let it be done, yeah.
I tell you who we are under the sun,
We are the children of the Rastaman.
We are the children of the higher man.

Africa unite, Africa unite.
Unite for the benefit of your people.
Unite for it's later than you think.

We are the children of the higher man.
Africa unite, Africa unite.
Unite for the benefit of your people.
Unite for it's later than you think.

2
BELLY FULL
(THEM BELLY FULL
(BUT WE HUNGRY))

Na-na-na-na-na-na-na-na-na,
Na-na-na-na-na-na-na-na-na,
Na-na-na-na-na-na-na-na-na,
Na-na-na-na-na-na-na-na-na.

Them belly full but we hungry,
A hungry mob is a angry mob.
A rain a-fall but the dirt it tough,
A pot a-cook but the food no 'nough.

You're gonna dance to Jah music, dance,
We're gonna dance to Jah music, dance.

Forget your troubles and dance,
Forget your sorrow and dance.
Forget your sickness and dance,
Forget your weakness and dance.

Cost of living get so high,
Rich and poor, they start a-cry.
Now the weak must get strong.
They say, 'Oh, what a tribulation.'

Them belly full but we hungry,
A hungry mob is a angry mob.
A rain a-fall but the dirt it tough,
A pot a-cook but the food no 'nough.

We're gonna chuck to Jah music, chuckin',
We're chuckin' to Jah music, we're chuckin'.
Chuckin', chuckin',
Chuckin', chuckin'.

A belly full but them hungry,
A hungry mob is a angry mob.
A rain a-fall but the dirt it tough,
A pot a-cook but the food no 'nough.

A angry man is a angry man,
A rain a-fall but the dirt it tough.

3
BUFFALO SOLDIER

Buffalo soldier, dreadlock rasta.
There was a buffalo soldier in the heart of America.
Stolen from Africa,
Brought to America,
Fighting on arrival,
Fighting for survival.

I mean it, when I analyse the stench,
To me, it makes a lot of sense.
How the dreadlock rasta
Was the buffalo soldier.

And he was taken from Africa,
Brought to America.
Fighting on arrival,
Fighting for survival.
Said he was a buffalo soldier in the heart of America.

If you know your history,
Then you would know where you comin' from,
Then you wouldn't have to ask me
Who the heck do I think I am.

I'm just a buffalo soldier in the heart of America,
Stolen from Africa,
Brought to America,
Said he was fighting on arrival,
Fighting for survival.

Said he was a buffalo soldier,
Win the war for America.

Dreadie, woe-yoe-yoe,
Woe-yoe-yoe-yoe,
Woe-yoe-yoe-yoe-yoe-yoe-yoe-yoe.

Buffalo soldier, troddin' thru' the land, oh.
Said he wanna ran, and then you wanna hand,
Troddin' thru' the land, yea, yea.
Said he was a buffalo soldier,
Win the war for America.
Buffalo soldier, dreadlock rasta.

Fighting on arrival,
Fighting for survival.
Driven from the mainland
To the heart of the Caribbean.

Singing, woe-yoe-yoe,
Woe-yoe-yoe-yoe,
Woe-yoe-yoe-yoe-yoe-yoe-yoe-yoe.

Troddin' thru' San Juan
In the arms of America.
Troddin' thru' Jamaica,
A buffalo soldier.
Fighting on arrival,
Fighting for survival.
Buffalo soldier, dreadlock rasta.

Woe-yoe-yoe,
Woe-yoe-yoe-yoe,
Woe-yoe-yoe-yoe-yoe-yoe-yoe-yoe.

4
COMING IN
FROM THE COLD

In this life,
In this life,
In this life,
In this life oh sweet life we're coming in from the cold.

We're coming in, we're coming in,
We're coming in, we're coming in,
We're coming in, we're coming in,
We're coming in, we're coming in from the cold.

It's you, it's you,
It's you I'm talkin' to.
Well, it's you, you,
You I'm talkin' to now.

Why do you look so sad
And forsaken?
When one door is closed
Don't you know
Another is opened?

Would you let the system make you kill your
    brother man?
No, dread, no,
Would you make the system make you kill your
    brother man?
No, dread, no.

Would you make the system get on top of your
    head again?
No, dread, no.
Well the biggest man you ever did see was,
Was a-just a baby.

In this life,
In this,
In this life,
Oh, sweet life coming in from the cold.

We're coming in, we're coming in,
We're coming in, we're coming in,
Coming in, woo,
Coming in from the cold.

It's life, it's life,
It's life, it's life,
It's life, it's life,
It's life, it's woah,
Well coming in from the cold.

We're coming in, we're coming in,
We're coming in, we're coming in, woo,
Coming in, coming in,
Coming in from the cold.

It's you, it's you,
It's you I'm talkin' to.
Well, it's you, you,
You I'm talkin' to now.

(continued overleaf)

Why do you look so sad
And forsaken?
When one door is closed
Don't you know
Many more is opened?

Would you let the system get on top of your
    head again?
No, dread, no,
Would you let the system make you kill your
    brother man?
No, dread, no.

Would you make the system get on top of your
    head again?
No, dread, no.
Well the biggest man you ever did see was,
Was a-just a baby.

In this life,
In this,
In this life,
Oh, sweet life coming in from the cold.

We're coming in, we're coming in,
We're coming in, we're coming in,
Coming in, woo,
Coming in from the cold.

We're coming in, we're coming in,
We're coming in, we're coming in,
We're coming in, we're coming in,
Wooh, yeah, coming in from the cold.

We're coming in, we're coming in,
We're coming in, we're coming in,
We're coming in, we're coming in,
Woh, yeah, coming in from the cold.

5
CONCRETE JUNGLE

No sun will shine in my day today. No sun will shine.
The high yellow moon won't come out to play.
    Won't come out to play.
Darkness has covered my light.
And has changed, and has changed my day into night.
Now where is this love to be found,
Won't someone tell me?

'Cause life must be somewhere to be found, yeah.
Instead of a concrete jungle where the livin' is hardest.
Concrete jungle, oh man,
You've got to do your best, yeah.

No chains around my feet, but I'm not free.
I know I am bound here in captivity.
And I've never known happiness,
And I've never known sweet caresses.
Still, I be always laughing like a clown,
Won't someone help me?

'Cause I've, I've got to pick myself from off the
    ground, yeah.
In this here concrete jungle, I say, what do you got
    for me now?
Concrete jungle, oh,
Why won't you let me be now?

No chains around my feet, but I'm not free.
I know I am bound here in captivity.
And I've never known happiness,
And I've never known sweet caresses.
Still, I be always laughing like a clown,
Won't someone help me?

'Cause I've, I've got to pick myself from off the
    ground, yeah.
In this here concrete jungle, I say, what do you got
    for me now?
Concrete jungle, oh,
Why won't you let me be now?

'Cause I've, I've got to pick myself from off the
    ground, yeah.
In this here concrete jungle, I say, what do you got
    for me now?
Concrete jungle, oh,
Why won't you let me be now?

Concrete jungle,
You name it,
In this concrete jungle.
Concrete jungle,
You name it,
We got it,
Concrete jungle now.

COULD YOU BE LOVED

EXODUS

Could you be loved,
And be loved?
Could you be loved,
And be loved?

Don't let them fool you,
Or even try to school you, oh, no.
We've got a mind of our own,
So go to hell if what you're thinkin' isn't right.
Love would never leave us alone,
In the darkness there must come out to light.

Could you be loved,
And be loved?
Could you be loved,
And be loved?

The road of life is rocky,
And you must stumble too.
So while you point your fingers, someone else is
    judgin' you.
Love your brother man.

Could you be, could you be loved?
Could you be, could you be, could you be loved?
Could you be, could you be loved?

Don't let them change you,
Or even try to rearrange you, oh, no.
We've got a life to live,
Ooh, ooh ooh.
They say only, only,
Only the fittest of the fittest shall survive.
Stay alive, oh.

Could you be loved,
And be loved?
Could you be loved,
And be loved?

You ain't gonna miss your water
Until your well runs dry.
No matter how you treat him,
The man will never be satisfied.

Could you be, could you be, could you be loved?
Could you be, could you be loved?
Could you be, could you be, could you be loved?
Could you be, could you be loved?

Say somethin', say somethin'.
Say somethin', say somethin'.

Exodus, movement of Jah people, oh yeah.
Open your eyes and let me tell you this.

Men and people will fight ya down.
Tell me why. When you see Jah light.
Let me tell you, if you're not wrong.
Then why? Everything is alright.
So we gonna walk, alright,
Through the roads of creation.
We're the generation. Tell me why!
Trod through great tribulation.

Exodus, movement of Jah people.
Exodus, movement of Jah people.

Open your eyes.
And look within.
Are you satisfied
With the life you're living?
We know where we're going.
We know where we're from.
We're leaving Babylon,
We're going to our father-land.

Exodus, movement of Jah people.

Movement of Jah people.

Moses.
Movement of Jah people.
Gonna cross the Red Sea.
Movement of Jah people.
Send us another brother Moses.
Movement of Jah people.
Gonna cross the Red Sea.
Movement of Jah people.

Move! Move! Move!
Move! Move! Move!

Open your eyes,
Tell men why. And look within.
Are you satisfied
With the life you're living?
We know where we're going.
We know where we're from.
We're leaving Babylon,
We're going to our father-land.

Exodus, movement of Jah people.
Exodus, movement of Jah people.

Move! Move! Move!

Movement of Jah people.
Move!

8
EASY SKANKING

Easy skanking, skanking it easy.
Easy skanking, skanking it slow.
Easy skanking, skanking it easy.
Easy skanking, skanking it slow.

Excuse me while I light my spliff.
Oh God, I've got to take a lift.
From reality I just can't drift.
That's why I'm stayin' with this riff.
Take it easy.

Lord, now take it easy.
Take it easy. Got to take it easy.
See, we're takin' it easy.
We're takin' it slow.
We're takin' it easy.
Got to take it slow. So, take it easy.
Oh, take it easy.
Take it easy. Take it easy.

Excuse me while I light my spliff.
Oh God, I've got to take a lift.
From reality I just can't drift.
That's why I'm stayin' with this riff.
Take it easy.

Got to take it easy.
Take it easy. Skanking, taking it slow.
Tell you what. Herb for my wine,
Honey for my strong drink,
Herb for my wine,
Honey for my strong drink. Take it easy.
Skanking take it easy.
Take it easy. Take it easy.

Takin' it easy.
Skankin' it slow.

9
GET UP, STAND UP

Get up, stand up, stand up for your right.
Get up, stand up, stand up for your right.
Get up, stand up, stand up for your right.
Get up, stand up, don't give up the fight.

Preacher man, don't tell me heaven is under the earth.
I know you don't know what life is really worth.
Is not all that glitters is gold?
And half the story has never been told.
So now you see the light, aay.
Stand up for your right.

Come on, get up, stand up, stand up for your right.
Get up, stand up, don't give up the fight.
Get up, stand up, stand up for your right.
Get up, stand up, don't give up the fight.

Most people think great God will come from the sky,
Take away ev'rything, and make ev'rybody feel high.
But if you know what life is worth,
You would look for yours on earth.
And now you see the light,
You stand up for your right.

Yah, get up, stand up, stand up for your right.
Get up, stand up, don't give up the fight.
Get up, stand up, stand up for your right.
Get up, stand up, don't give up the fight.

We're sick and tired of your is-m and skism game.
Die and go to heaven in Jesus' name, Lord.
We know when we understand. Almighty God is a
    living man.
You can fool some people sometimes,
But you can't fool all the people all the time.
So now we see the light. We gonna stand up for
    our right.

So, you'd better get up, stand up, stand up for
    your right.
Get up, stand up, don't give up the fight.

Get up, stand up, stand up for your right.
Get up, stand up, don't give up the fight.

10
GUAVA JELLY

You said you love me, I said I love you.

Why won't you stop your crying?
Dry your weeping eyes,
You know that I love, I love,
I love, I love you so.

Da-da-dam da-da-damsel. Here I am.
Me said, 'Come rub it 'pon me belly with you
   Guava Jelly,
Da-da-da-da-da-damsel. Here I stand,
Come rub it 'pon me belly with you Guava Jelly'.

I really, really, I really love you.
Yes, I really, really love you, child.

I'll say you should stop, stop crying.
Wipe, wipe your weeping eyes,
You'll see how I'm gonna love,
Love you from the bottom of my heart,

Da-da-dam da-da-damsel. Here I am.
Me said, 'Come rub it 'pon me belly with you
   Guava Jelly,
Da-da-da-da-damsel. Here I stand,
Come rub it 'pon me belly with you Guava Jelly'.

Come-a, come-a, come-a, come-a damsel, oh darling.

Here I am.
Said 'Come rub it 'pon me belly with you Guava Jelly'.

11
I SHOT THE SHERIFF

I shot the sheriff, but I didn't shoot no deputy.
Oh, no, oh.
I shot the sheriff, but I didn't shoot no deputy.
Oh, no, oh. Yeah.

All around in my hometown they're tryin' to track
   me down, yeah.
They say they want to bring me in guilty for the
   killing of a deputy,
For the life of a deputy.

But I say, oh, now, now.
Oh, I shot the sheriff, but I swear it was in self defence.
Ooh, ooh, ooh.
I said, I shot the sheriff, oh Lord, and they say it is
   a capital offence.
Ohh, ooh, ooh.
Hear this.

Sheriff John Brown always hated me, for what
   I don't know.
Ev'ry time I plant a seed, he said, 'Kill it before
   it grows.'
He said, 'Kill them before they grow.'

And so, oh, now, now. Read it in the news.
I shot the sheriff, but I swear it was in self defence.
Ooh, ooh, ooh.
I shot the sheriff, but I swear it was in self defence.

Freedom came my way one day and I started
   out of town, yeah!
All of a sudden I saw Sheriff John Brown aimin'
   to shoot me down.
So I shot, I shot, I shot him down.
And I say, if I am guilty I will pay.

I shot the sheriff, but I say, but I didn't shoot
   no deputy.
Oh, no, oh.
I shot the sheriff, but I didn't shoot no deputy.
Ooo, oo, ooh.

Reflexes had the better of me. And what is to be
   must be.
Ev'ry day the bucket ago a well, one day the bottom
   ago drop out.
One day the bottom ago drop out.
I say, I, I.

I, I shot the sheriff, but I didn't shoot the deputy.

12
I'M HURTING INSIDE

When I was just a little child,
Happiness was there a while.
Then from me, yeah, it slipped one day.
Happiness, come back, I say.

'Cause if you don't come, I've got to go lookin'
    for happiness,
Well, if you don't come, I've got to go lookin', Lord,
For happiness, happiness.
I'm hurting inside. I'm hurting inside.

Oh, hear my cry, hear my cry,
Yeah, my, my, my, my, my, my, my, my cry.

Been together like school children,
Then you hurt me just in vain,
Lord, I'm your weary child.
Happiness, come back a while.

'Cause if you don't come, I've got to go lookin'
    for happiness,
Well, if you don't come, I've got to go lookin', Lord,
For happiness, happiness.
I'm hurting inside. I'm hurting inside.

I'm hurting inside.
I'm hurting inside.

I'm hurting inside.

13
I'M STILL WAITING

I'm still waiting, I'm still waiting,
I'm still waiting, I'm still waiting for you,
Nobody else but you, oh.

My feet won't keep me up any more.
Ev'ry little beat my heart beats, girl, it's at your door.
I just wanna love you and I'm never gonna hurt you,
    girl.
So won't you come out to me now, girl?
Oh, can't you see I'm under your spell?
But, I got to, got to go.

Why, girl, oh, why girl?
You know, you know how I love you.
That's why I wait my whole life through.
My parting to you
For being what I am,
But don't you know I'm waiting?

I'm still waiting, I'm still waiting,
I'm still waiting, I'm still waiting

14
IS THIS LOVE?

I wanna love you, and treat you right.
I wanna love you, every day and every night.
We'll be together, with a roof right over our heads.
We'll share the shelter of my single bed.
We'll share the same room,
Jah provide the bread.

Is this love, is this love, is this love, is this love that
    I'm feelin'?
Is this love, is this love, is this love, is this love that
    I'm feelin'?

I wanna know, wanna know, wanna know now.
I got to know, got to know, got to know now.
I, I'm willing and able,
So I throw my cards on your table.

I wanna love you, and treat you right.
I wanna love you, every day and every night.
We'll be together, with a roof right over our heads.
We'll share the shelter of my single bed.
We'll share the same room,
Jah provide the bread.

Is this love, is this love, is this love, is this love that
    I'm feelin'?
Is this love, is this love, is this love, is this love that
    I'm feelin'?

I wanna know, wanna know, wanna know now.
I got to know, got to know, got to know now.
I, I'm willing and able,
So I throw my cards on your table.

See, I wanna love you . . .

15
IRON LION ZION

Well, I'm on the rock,
And then, I check the stock.
I had to run like a fugitive
To save the life I live.

I'm gonna be iron, like a lion, in Zion,
I'm gonna be iron, like a lion, in Zion, oh yeah.
Lion, iron, Zion, lion, Zion.

I'm on the run,
But I ain't got no gun.
See, they want to be the star
So they fighting tribal war,
And they saying,

'Iron, like a lion, in Zion.
Iron, like a lion, in Zion.'
Iron, lion, Zion.

I'm on the rock,
I check a stock.
I had to run like a fugitive,
Just to, just to save the life I live, oh now.

And still I'm gonna be iron like a lion in Zion.
I'm gonna be iron, like a lion in Zion.
What did you say?
 Iron, lion, Zion.

I'm on the run,
But I don't got no gun.
See, my brothers want to be the stars,
So they fighting tribal war,
And they saying,

'Iron, like a lion, in Zion.
Iron, like a lion, in Zion.'
Steal them off me.
Iron, lion, Zion.

Iron, lion, Zion.
I'm on the run.
Got no gun.
Iron, lion, Zion.

16
JAMMING

Well alright. We're jammin'.
I wanna jam it with you.
We're jammin', jammin',
And I hope you like jammin', too.

Ain't no rules, ain't no vow,
We can do it anyhow.
I and I will see you through,
'Cause every day we pay the price,
We are the living sacrifice,
Jammin' till the jam is through.

We're jammin'.
To think that jammin' was a thing of the past.
We're jammin',
And I hope this jam is gonna last,

No bullet can stop us now,
We neither beg nor we won't bow,
Neither can be bought nor sold.
We all defend the right,
Jah Jah children must unite,
For life is worth much more than gold.

We're jammin', jammin', jammin', jammin'.
And we're jammin' in the name of the Lord.
We're jammin', jammin', jammin', jammin'.
We're jammin' right straight from the yard.

Holy Mount Zion, Holy Mount Zion.
Jah sit-teth in Mount Zion and rules all creation.
Yeah, we're, we're jammin'.

Bop-chu-wa-wa-wa. We're jammin'.
I wanna jam it with you.
We're jammin',
And jam down, hope you're jammin' too.

Jah knows how much I've tried,
The truth cannot hide,
To keep you satisfied.
True love that now exists
Is the love I can't resist,
So jam by my side.

We're jammin', jammin', jammin', jammin'.
I wanna jam it with you.
We're jammin', we're jammin', we're jammin',
    we're jammin',
We're jammin', we're jammin', we're jammin',
    we're jammin'.
Hope you like jammin' too.

17
LICK SAMBA

Lick samba, lick samba, lick samba; oh, lick samba.
Ah, me say, lick samba, lick samba, oh yeah.
I could not resist,
Oh, now, another like this, oh now.

And though I know you'll hurt me again,
I'll go on. I'll feel the pain.
And it's not that I am weak,
But it's that I'm on a peak, oh darlin'.

A-just a lick samba, lick samba, lick samba,
Oh, lick samba. Oh lick samba; oh lick samba.

Bring it up a licky one time.
I'll set a little flame.
You can write it down in my name,
Morning time, noon or night.

A-just a lick samba, lick samba, lick samba,
Oh, lick samba. Oh lick samba; oh lick samba.

Lick samba, lick samba, lick samba, oh, lick samba.
Oh, lick samba. If it's morning time, I'm ready.
Oh, lick samba. And if it's late at night, I'm steady.
Oh, lick samba.

LIVELY UP YOURSELF

Oh, lively up yourself and don't be no drag,
Lively up yourself, reggae is another bag.
Lively up yourself and don't say no.
Lively up yourself 'cause I said so.

You, what you gonna do?
You rock so, you rock so, like you never did before.
You dip, so, you dip so,
Till you dip through my door.
You skank so, you skank so, oh yeah.
You come so, you come so, come alive today.

And lively up yourself
A-lot-a, a-lot-a, a-lot-a, a-lot-a.
Lively up yourself, did you know, did you know?
Lively up yourself, 'cause if you don't do it,
Ain't nobody gonna do it for you.

Lively up yourself and don't be no,
Don't be no, don't be no, don't be no, no drag.
What you got that I don't know? I'm a-tryin'
    to wonder,
Wonder why you, wonder, wonder why you act so.
And don't be no drag.
Lively up yourself, for reggae is another bag.

You're gonna rock so, you rock so,
Like you never did before.
You dip so, you dip so,
Till you dip through my door.
You skank so, you skank so, oh yeah.
You come so, you come so, come alive today.

And lively up yourself, your woman in the
    morning time, y'all.
Keep a-lively up yourself and when the evening
    come and take ya,
Take ya, take ya, take ya.
Come on baby, I wanna be lively myself.
Come on babe, I wanna be lively myself.
Lively up yourself.

MELLOW MOOD

I'll play your fav'rite song, darlin'.
We can rock it all night long, darlin'.

'Cause I've got love, darlin',
Love, sweet love, darlin'.
Mellow mood has got me,
So let the music rock me.
'Cause I've got love darlin',
Love, sweet love, darlin'.
Quiet as the night,
Please turn off your light.

I'll play your fav'rite song, darlin'.
We can rock it all night long, darlin'.

Strike the hammer while iron is hot.
Strike the hammer while iron is hot.
Strike the hammer while iron is hot.

Open up your heart. Open up your heart.
Let love come running in, darlin',
Love, sweet love, darlin',
Love, sweet love, darlin'.

Strike the hammer while iron is hot.
Strike the hammer while iron is hot.
Strike the hammer while iron is hot.

Open up your heart. Open up your heart.
Let love come running in, darlin',
Love, sweet love, darlin',
Love, sweet love, darlin'.

Strike the hammer while iron is hot.
Strike the hammer while iron is hot.
Strike the hammer while iron is hot.

Open up your heart. Open up your heart.
Let love come running in, darlin',
Love, sweet love, darlin',
Love, sweet love, darlin'.

Mellow mood has got me, darlin'.
Let the music rock me, darlin,
'Cause I got you love, darlin'.

Love, sweet love, darlin'.

20
NATURAL MYSTIC

There's a nat'ral mystic blowing through the air.

If you listen carefully now, you will hear.
This could be the first trumpet, might as well be
   the last.
Many more will have to suffer, many more will
   have to die.
Don't ask me why.
Things are not the way they used to be.
I won't tell no lie.

One and all got to face reality now.
Though I try to find the answer to all the questions
   they ask,
Though I know it's impossible to go living through
   the past.
Don't tell no lie.
There's a nat'ral mystic blowing through the air.
Can't keep them down.

If you listen carefully now, you will hear.
Such a nat'ral mystic blowing through the air.
This could be the first trumpet, might as well be
   the last.
Many more will have to suffer, many more will
   have to die.
Don't ask me why.
There's a nat'ral mystic blowing through the air.
I won't tell no lie.

If you listen carefully now, you will hear.
There's a nat'ral mystic blowing through the air.
Such a nat'ral mystic blowing through the air.

There's a nat'ral mystic blowing through the air.
Such a nat'ral mystic blowing through the air.

21
NO WOMAN, NO CRY

No woman, no cry.
No woman, no cry.

Said, said, said I remember when we used to sit
In the government yard in Trenchtown.
Oba, observing the hypocrites
As they would mingle with the good people we meet.
Good friends we had,
Oh good friends we've lost along the way.
In this bright future you can't forget your past
So, dry your tears I say.

And no woman, no cry.
No woman, no cry.

Said, said, said I remember when we used to sit
In the government yard in Trenchtown.
Oba, observing the hypocrites
As they would mingle with the good people we meet.
Good friends we had,
Oh good friends we've lost along the way.
In this bright future you can't forget your past
So, dry your tears I say.

And, ev'rything's gonna be alright.
Ev'rything's gonna be alright.

No woman, no cry.
No woman, no cry.
Here little darlin', don't shed no tears.
No woman, no cry.

Said, said, said I remember when we used to sit
In the government yard in Trenchtown.
And then Georgie would make a firelight
As it was log wood burnin' through the night.
Then we would cook cornmeal porridge
Of which I'll share with you.
My feet is my only carriage,
So, I've got to push on through, but while I'm gone.

I mean, ev'rything's gonna be alright.
Ev'rything's gonna be alright.
Ev'rything's gonna be alright.
Ev'rything's gonna be alright, so, woman, no cry.

No, no woman,
No woman, no cry.
Oh, my little sister don't shed no tears.
No woman, no cry.

Said, said, said I remember when we used to sit
In the government yard in Trenchtown.
And then Georgie would make a firelight
As it was log wood burnin' through the night.
Then we would cook cornmeal porridge
Of which I'll share with you.
My feet is my only carriage,
So, I've got to push on through, but while I'm gone.

I mean, no woman, no cry.
No woman, no cry.
Oh, my little darlin', I say don't shed no tears.
No woman, no cry. Yeah.

Little darlin', don't shed no tears.
No woman, no cry.

22
NICE TIME

Long time we no have no nice time,
Doo yoo-dee-dun-doo-yea.
Think about that.
Long time we no have no nice time,
Doo yoo-dee-dun-doo-yea.
Think about that.

This is my heart to rock you steady.
I'll give you love the time you're ready.
This little heart in me just won't let me be.
I'm just to rock you, now.
Won't you rock with me?

Long time we no have no nice time,
Doo yoo-dee-dun-doo-yea.
Think about that.

This is my heart to rock you steady.
I'll give you love the time you're ready.
This little heart in me just won't let me be.
I'm just to rock you, now.
Won't you rock with me?

Long time we no have no nice time,
Doo yoo-dee-dun-doo-yea.
Think about that.

23
ONE LOVE

One love, one heart.
Let's get together and feel alright.
Hear the children crying. One love.
Hear the children crying. One heart.

Sayin', 'Give thanks and praise to the Lord and
    I will feel alright.'
Sayin', 'Let's get together and feel alright.'
Whoa, whoa, whoa, whoa.
Let them all pass all their dirty remarks. One love.
There is one question I'd really love to ask. One heart
Is there a place for the hopeless sinner
Who has hurt all mankind just to save his own?
    Believe me.

One love, one heart.
Let's get together and feel alright.
As it was in the beginning. One love.
So shall it be in the end. One heart.

Alright, 'Give thanks and praise to the Lord and
    I will feel alright.'
Sayin', 'Let's get together and feel alright.'
One more thing.
Let's get together to fight this holy Armageddon.
    One love.
So when the Man comes there will be no, no doom.
    One song.
Have pity on those whose chances grow thinner.
There ain't no hiding place from the Father of
    Creation.

Sayin', One love, one heart.
Let's get together and feel alright.
I'm pleading to mankind. One love.
Oh, Lord. One heart.

Whoa. 'Give thanks and praise to the Lord and
    I will feel alright.'
Let's get together and feel alright.

24
PLEASE DON'T
ROCK MY BOAT

Please don't you rock my boat,
'Cause I don't want my boat to be rockin' anyhow.
Please don't you rock-a my boat, no,
'Cause I don't want my boat to be rockin'.

I'm tellin' you that oh, ooh, oh, I like it a-like this.
Can you miss?
And you should know, ooh, oh,
When I like it a-like a-this,
I'm a-really is, ooh, yeah.
You sa-tis, sa-tis satisfy my soul till morning time.
Evening goes, satisfy my soul.
Yes, I been a-tellin' you.

Bake me the sweetest cake,
Happy inside all the time.
Oh, can't you see what you've done for me, yeah.
You make me feel like
When we bend a new corner,
We feel like sweep-stake winners, yeah.
When we bend a new corner,
We feel like sweep-stake winners.

And I say oh, ooh, oh, I like it a-like this.
Yes I do.
And you should know, ooh, oh,
When I like it a-like a-this,
I've got it. Just can't miss, ooh.
You sa-tis, satisfy my soul, darlin'.
Make me love you in the mornin' time, yeah.
If ever I treated you bad, make it up to you one time.

'Cause I'm happy inside all the time.
I want you beside me, yeah, to be mine.
One thing you got to do,
When we are holding hands together,
You've got to know that we love,
We love each other, yeah.
And if ev'ry time you should walk away from me,
You know I need your sympathy, yeah.

Can you see it?
Do you believe me?
Oh, darlin', darlin',
I'm callin', callin'.
Satisfy my soul, satisfy my soul.
Never, never, never give it up now.

We're all in the same boat,
Rockin' on the same rope.
We've got together, loving each other.
And can't you see what I've got for you, yeah.
I'm happy, happy, happy, happy, happy,
Happy and not even time to be blue yeah.

25
REDEMPTION SONG

Old pirates, yes, they rob I.
Sold I to the merchant ships
Minutes after they took I
From the bottomless pit.
But my hand was made strong by the hand of the
    Almighty.
We forward in this generation triumphantly.

Won't you help to sing
These songs of freedom?
'Cause all I ever had,
Redemption songs, redemption songs.

Emancipate yourselves from mental slav'ry,
None but ourselves can free our minds.
Have no fear for atomic energy,
'Cause none of them can stop the time.
How long shall they kill our prophets while we stand
    aside and look?
Some say it's just a part of it, we've got to fulfil
    the book.

Won't you help to sing
These songs of freedom?
'Cause all I ever had,
Redemption songs, redemption songs, redemption
    songs.

Emancipate yourselves from mental slav'ry,
None but ourselves can free our minds.
Have no fear for atomic energy,
'Cause none of them can stop the time.
How long shall they kill our prophets while we stand
    aside and look?
Some say it's just a part of it, we've got to fulfil
    the book.

Won't you help to sing
These songs of freedom?
'Cause all I ever had,
Redemption songs, all I ever had,
Redemption songs,
These songs of freedom, songs of freedom.

26
SO MUCH TROUBLE IN THE WORLD

So much trouble in the world.
So much trouble in the world.

Bless my eyes this morning,
Jah sun is on the rise once again.
The way earthly things are going,
Anything can happen.
You see men sailing on their ego trips,
Blast off on their spaceships,
Million miles from reality;
No care for care for you, no care for me.

So much trouble in the world.
So much trouble in the world.

All you got to do is give a little, take a little,
Give a little, one more time.
Give a little, take a little,
Give a little.

So you think you found the solution,
But it's just another illusion.
So before you check out this tide,
Don't leave another corner stone standing there
    behind.

We've got to face the day,
Ooh wee, come what may.
We the street people talking,
We the people struggling.
Now, they're sitting on a time bomb,
Now I know the time has come,
What goes on up is coming on down,
Goes around and comes around.

So much trouble in the world.
So much trouble in the world.

There is so much trouble in the world.
So much trouble in the world.

27
SMALL AXE

Why boasteth thyself, oh evil men,
Playing smart and not being clever?
I say you're working iniquity to achieve vanity, yeah,
But the goodness of Jah Jah endureth forever.

If you are the big tree, we are the small axe,
Sharpened to cut you down, ready to cut you down,
These are the words of my master.
Keep on telling me no weak heart shall prosper,
    oh, no they can't.
And whosoever diggeth a pit,
Lord, shall fall in it, shall fall in it.
Whosoever diggeth a pit
Shall bury in it, shall bury in it.

If you are the big tree, we are the small axe,
Sharpened to cut you down, ready to cut you down,
These are the words of my master.
Keep on telling me no weak heart shall prosper,
    oh, no they can't.
And whosoever diggeth a pit,
Lord, shall fall in it, shall fall in it.
Whosoever diggeth a pit
Shall bury in it, shall bury in it.

If you have a big tree, we have a small axe,
Ready to cut you down, sharpened to cut you down.

If you are the big tree, we have a small axe,
Ready to cut you down sharpened to cut you down.

28
SOUL REBEL

Soul rebel, soul rebel.
I'm a capturer, soul adventurer.
I'm a rebel, soul rebel.
I'm a capturer, soul adventurer.

See the morning sun,
See the morning sun, on the hillside.
If you're not living good, gotta travel wide,
You gotta travel wide.

Said I'm a living man,
Said I'm a living man and I've got,
I've got work to do.
If you're not happy,
Then you must be blue,
Must be blue, people say.

Soul rebel, soul rebel.
I'm a capturer, soul adventurer.
I'm a rebel, soul rebel.
I'm a capturer, soul adventurer.

See the morning sun,
See the morning sun, on the hillside.
If you're not living good, gotta travel wide,
You gotta travel wide.

Said I'm a living man,
Said I'm a living man and I've got,
I've got work to do.
If you're not happy,
Then you must be blue,
Must be blue, people say.

I'm a rebel, soul rebel.
I'm a capturer, soul adventurer.

29
SUN IS SHINING

Sun is shining, the weather is sweet.
Make sure you want to move your dancing feet.
To the rescue, here I am.
Want you to know, y'all, where I stand.

Monday morning, here I am.
Tuesday evening, want you to know just if you can,
Where I stand.
Wednesday morning, tell myself a new day is rising.
Thursday evening, get on the rise, a new day is
    dawning.
Friday morning, here I am.
Saturday evening, want you to know just,
Want you to know just where I stand.

When the morning gathers the rainbow,
Want you to know I'm a rainbow, too.
So, to the rescue, here I am.
Want you to know just if you can, where I stand,
Know, know, know, know, know, know, know,
    know.

We'll lift our heads and give Jah praises,
We'll lift our heads and give Jah praises, yeah.
Sun is shining, the weather is sweet.
Make you want to move your dancing feet.
To the rescue, here I am.
Want you to know just if you can where I stand,
No, no, no, no, where I stand.

Sun is shining, sun is shining.

STIR IT UP

Stir it up, little darling, stir it up.
Come on and stir it up, little darling, stir it up.

It's been a long, long time
Since I've got you on my mind,
And now you are here,
I say, it's so clear,
See what we can do, honey,
Just me and you.

Come on and stir it up, little darling, stir it up.
Come on and stir it up, little darling, stir it up.

I'll push the wood, I'll blaze your fire,
Then I'll satisfy your, your heart's desire.
Said I'll stir it, yeah,
Ev'ry minute, yeah.
All you got to do, honey,
Is keep it in.

And stir it up, little darling, stir it up.
Come on and stir it up, ooh, little darling, stir it up.
   Yeah.

Oh, will you quench me,
While I'm thirsty?
Or would you cool me down when I'm hot?
Your recipe, darling,
Is so tasty,
And you sure can stir your pot.

So stir it up, little darling, stir up.
Come on and stir it up, ooh, little darling, stir it up.

Come on and stir it up, ooh, little darling, stir it up.
Stir it up, little darling, stir it up.
Come on and stir it up, ooh, little darling, stir it up.
Stir it up, little darling, stir it up.
Come on and stir it up, ooh, little darling, stir it up.
Stir it up, little darling, stir it up.

THANK YOU LORD

Thank you Lord.
Thank you Lord.

Thank you Lord, for what you've done for me.
Thank you Lord, for what you're doing now.
Thank you, for ev'ry little thing.
Thank you, Lord, for ev'ry song I sing.

Say I'm in no competition,
But I made my decision.
You can keep your opinion.
I'm just calling on the wise man's communion.

Thank you, Lord, for what you've done for me.
Ev'ry day when I pray.
Thank you Lord, for what you're doing now.
In my prayers I say;
Thank you, Lord, for ev'ry little thing.
Thank you, Lord, for ev'ry song I sing.

Sing along, sing along.
Sing along, sing along.
Sing along, sing along.

Said I can't find the explanation, Lord have mercy,
To prove my appreciation.
Lord, in my simple way,
Yes, I am a-comin', comin', comin', comin'. I love
   to pray.

Thank you Lord.
Thank you, Lord, for what you're doing now.
All I can say;
Thank you, Lord, for ev'ry little thing.
Thank you, Lord, for ev'ry song I sing.

Sing along, sing along.
Sing along, sing along.
Sing along, sing along.

THREE LITTLE BIRDS

Don't worry about a thing,
'Cause ev'ry little thing gonna be alright.
Singin', 'Don't worry about a thing,
'Cause ev'ry little thing gonna be alright'.
Rise up this morning, smiled with the rising sun.
Three little birds pitch by my doorstep,
Singin' sweet songs of melodies pure and true, sayin',
'This is my message to you-oo-oo'.

Singin', 'Don't worry about a thing,
'Cause ev'ry little thing gonna be alright.
Singin', 'Don't worry about a thing,
'Cause ev'ry little thing gonna be alright'.
Rise up this morning, smiled with the rising sun.
Three little birds pitch by my doorstep,
Singin' sweet songs of melodies pure and true, sayin',
'This is my message to you-oo-oo'.

Singin', 'Don't worry about a thing,
'Cause ev'ry little thing gonna be alright.'

WAITING IN VAIN

I don't wanna wait in vain for your love.
I don't wanna wait in vain for your love.

From the very first time I blessed my eyes on you, girl,
My heart says, 'Follow through'.
But I know now that I'm way down on your line,
But the waiting feel is fine.
So don't treat me like a puppet on a string,
'Cause I know how to do my thing.
Don't talk to me as if you think I'm dumb,
I wanna know when you're gonna come.

See, I don't wanna wait in vain for your love.
I don't wanna wait in vain for your love.
I don't wanna wait in vain for your love.
'Cause it's summer is here.
I'm still waiting there.
Winter is here and I'm still waiting there.

Like I said, it's been three years since I'm knockin'
      on your door,
And I still can knock some more.
Ooh girl, ooh girl, is it feasible, I wanna know now,
For I to knock some more?
Ya see, in life I know there is lots of grief,
But your love is my relief.
Tears in my eyes burn, tears in my eyes burn
While I'm waiting while I'm waiting for my turn.

See, I don't wanna wait in vain for your love.
I don't wanna wait in vain for your love.
I don't wanna wait in vain for your love.
I don't wanna wait in vain for your love.

I don't wanna wait in vain for your love.
Oh, I don't wanna, I don't wanna, I don't wanna,
      I don't wanna,
I don't wanna wait in vain.
No, I don't wanna, I don't wanna, I don't wanna,
      I don't wanna,
I don't wanna wait in vain.

It's your love that I'm waiting on.
It's my love that you're running from.

34
WHO THE CAP FIT

Man to man is so unjust, children,
You don't know who to trust.
Your worst enemy could be your best friend,
And your best friend your worst enemy.
Some will eat and drink with you,
Then behind them su-su 'pon you.
Only your friend know your secrets,
So only he could reveal it.

And who the cap fit, let them wear it.
Who the cap fit, let them wear it.
Said I throw me corn, and then a gonna call no fowl.
I saying, 'Cok-cok-cok, cluk-cluk-cluk', yea.

Some will hate you, pretend they love you, now, then,
Behind they try to eliminate you.
But who Jah bless, no one curse,
Thank God, we're past the worse.
Hypocrites and parasites,
Will come up and take a bite.
And if your night should turn to day,
A lot of people would run away.

And who the cap fit, let them wear it.
Who the cap fit, let them wear it.
And then a gonna throw me corn, and then a gonna
    call no fowl.
And then a gonna, 'Cok-cok-cok, cluk-cluk-cluk'.

Some will eat and drink with you,
Then behind them su-su 'pon you.
And if your night should turn to day,
A lot of people would run away.

And who the cap fit, let them wear it.
Who the cap fit, let them wear it.
Said I throw me corn, me no call no fowl.
I saying, 'Cok-cok-cok, cluk-cluk-cluk'.

I saying, 'Cok-cok-cok, cluk-cluk-cluk.'

35
WHY SHOULD I?

Why should I bend down my head and cry?
Tell me why should I bend down my head and cry?

The old world has ended, the new world has just
    begun.
And all them people that live therein shall live
    on and on.
One more thing : Got to get what I need, got to get
    what I want.
Got to get what I need, got to get what I want.
Got to get satisfaction, got to get the action,
Got love and affection. One more thing.

Once there was two roads before us to pick our choice,
But good has overcome bad.
The sheep has heard their master's voice.
So tell me why.
Why should I bend down my head and cry?
No reason why.
Why should I bend down my head and cry?
Got to move, got to groove.

Got to get what I want.
Got to get it.
Got to get what I need.
Got to get it.
Got to get what I want.
Got to get it.
Got to get what I need.

The old world has ended, the new world has just
    begun.
And all them people that live therein shall live
    on and on.
One more thing.

Why should I bend down my head and cry?

THE MUSIC

1
AFRICA UNITE

WORDS & MUSIC BY BOB MARLEY
© COPYRIGHT 1979 BOB MARLEY MUSIC LIMITED.
BLUE MOUNTAIN MUSIC LIMITED, 47 BRITISH GROVE, LONDON W4.
ALL RIGHTS RESERVED. INTERNATIONAL COPYRIGHT SECURED.

Moderate Reggae

Instrumental

Af-ri-ca, u-nite, 'cause we're

mov-ing right out of Ba-by-lon, and we're go-ing to our fa-ther's land.

How good and how plea-sant it would be, be-fore God and man, yeah,
How good and how plea-sant it would be, be-fore God and man,

to see the u - ni-fi-ca-tion of all Af-ri-cans, yeah.
to see the u - ni-fi-ca-tion of all Ras-ta-man, yeah.

As it's been said al-rea-dy, let it be done, yeah. We are the child-ren of the
As it's been said al-rea-dy, let it be done, yeah. I tell you who we are

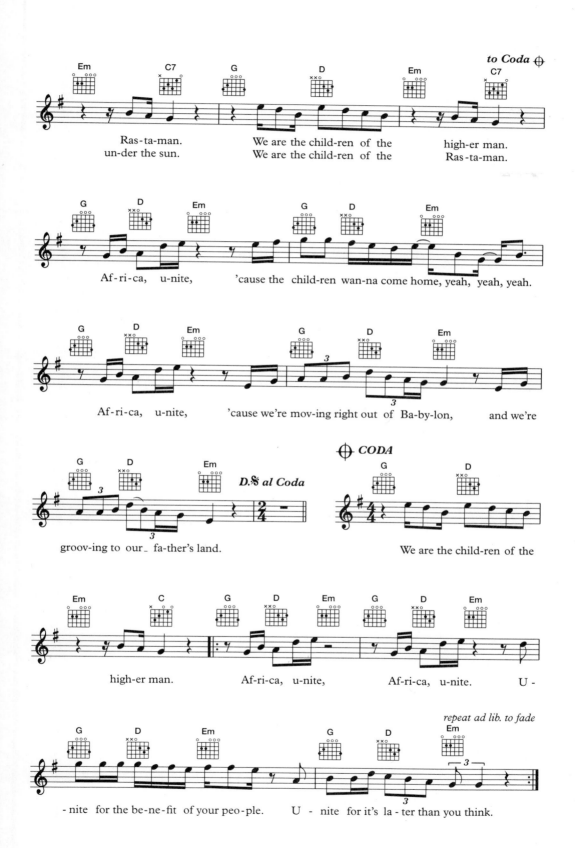

BELLY FULL
(THEM BELLY FULL (BUT WE HUNGRY))

WORDS & MUSIC BY LECON COGILL & CARLTON BARRETT
© COPYRIGHT 1974 BOB MARLEY MUSIC LIMITED.
BLUE MOUNTAIN MUSIC LIMITED, 47 BRITISH GROVE, LONDON W4.
ALL RIGHTS RESERVED. INTERNATIONAL COPYRIGHT SECURED.

Moderate Reggae

Instrumental

Na-na-na-na - na-na-na - na-na,   na-na-na-na - na-na-na - na-na,

na-na-na-na - na-na-na - na-na,   na-na-na-na - na-na-na - na-na.

Them bel-ly full but we hun - gry,_   a hun-gry mob is a an-gry mob.

A rain a-fall but the dirt it tough,   a pot a-cook but the food no 'nough. You're gon -

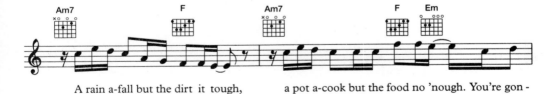

- na dance   to Jah mu - sic,   dance,   we're gon-na dance   to Jah mu - sic,

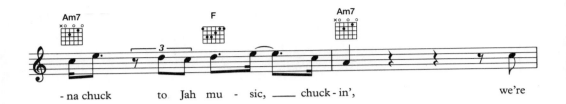

- na chuck to Jah mu - sic, ____ chuck - in', we're

chuck-in' to Jah mu - sic,__ we're chuck-in'.

Chuck-in', ____ chuck-in'. ____

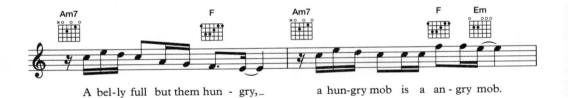

A bel-ly full but them hun - gry,_ a hun-gry mob is a an - gry mob.

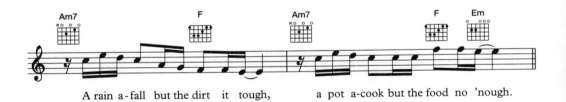

A rain a-fall but the dirt it tough, a pot a-cook but the food no 'nough.

repeat ad lib. to fade

A an-gry man is a an - gry man, a rain a-fall but the dirt it tough.

3

BUFFALO SOLDIER

WORDS & MUSIC BY BOB MARLEY & NOEL WILLIAMS.

Buf-fa-lo sol-dier, dread-lock ras-ta. There was a buf-fa-lo sol-dier in the heart of A-me-ri-ca. Sto-len from Af-ri-ca, brought to A-me-ri-ca, fight-ing on ar-ri-val, fight-ing for sur-vi-val. I mean it, when I a-na-lyse the stench, to me, it makes a lot of sense. How the dread-lock ras-

COMING IN FROM THE COLD

WORDS & MUSIC BY BOB MARLEY

5
CONCRETE JUNGLE

WORDS & MUSIC BY BOB MARLEY
© COPYRIGHT 1972 CAYMAN MUSIC INCORPORATED, USA.
BLUE MOUNTAIN MUSIC LIMITED, 47 BRITISH GROVE, LONDON W4.
ALL RIGHTS RESERVED. INTERNATIONAL COPYRIGHT SECURED.

COULD YOU BE LOVED

WORDS & MUSIC BY BOB MARLEY
© COPYRIGHT 1980 BOB MARLEY MUSIC LIMITED.
BLUE MOUNTAIN MUSIC LIMITED, 47 BRITISH GROVE, LONDON W4.
ALL RIGHTS RESERVED. INTERNATIONAL COPYRIGHT SECURED.

Stay a-live__ oh. Could you be loved

and be loved?_____

You ain't gon-na miss your wa - ter un -

- til your well runs dry.__ No mat-ter how you treat him, the man will

ne-ver be sa-tis-fied. Could you be, could you be, could you be loved?

repeat to fade

Could you be, could you be loved? Say some-thin', say some-thin'.

7

EXODUS

WORDS & MUSIC BY BOB MARLEY
© COPYRIGHT 1977 BOB MARLEY MUSIC LIMITED.
BLUE MOUNTAIN MUSIC LIMITED, 47 BRITISH GROVE, LONDON W4.

Moderate Reggae

Ex - o - dus,_ move-ment of Jah peo - ple, oh

_____ yeah._ O - pen your eyes and let me tell you this.

Men and peo - ple will fight ya down (Spoken) Tell me why.
(2.3.) O - pen your eyes,

when you see__ Jah light.__ Let me tell you, if you're
and look with - in.___ Are you sa - tis - fied

not wrong (Spoken) Then why? ev - 'ry - thing is al - right.
with the life you're liv - ing?

So we gon - na walk, al - right,_
We know where we're go - ing.

through the roads___ of cre - a - tion.
We know where we're from.___ We're

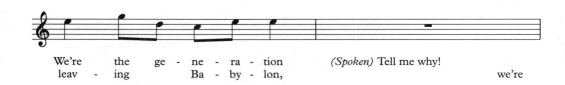

We're the ge - ne - ra - tion *(Spoken)* Tell me why! we're
leav - ing Ba - by - lon,

trod through great tri - bu - la - tion.
go - ing to our fa - ther - land.

Ex - o - dus,___ move - ment of Jah peo-

to Coda ⊕ | 1.2. *D.S* | 3.

- ple.

(Move - ment of Jah peo - ple.)
Send us an - oth - er Bro - ther

(Move - ment   of   Jah   peo - ple.)
Mo - ses.   Gon - na   cross___   the Red___   Sea.

(Move -   ment   of   Jah   peo - ple.)
Send us   an - oth - er   Bro - ther

- ple.)   Move!

CODA

Ex - o - dus,_

move-ment of Jah peo - ple.   Move!   Move!

repeat ad lib. to fade

Move!   (Move-ment of Jah peo - ple).
                   Move!

8
EASY SKANKING

WORDS & MUSIC BY BOB MARLEY
© COPYRIGHT 1977 BOB MARLEY MUSIC LIMITED.
BLUE MOUNTAIN MUSIC LIMITED, 47 BRITISH GROVE, LONDON W4.

Moderately fast

Ea - sy skank - ing, (skank-ing it ea - sy.) Ea - sy skank - ing,

(skank-ing it slow.) Ea - sy skank - ing, (skank-ing it ea - sy.)

Ea - sy skank - ing, (skank-ing it slow.) Ex - cuse me while I light my spliff.

Oh God, __ I've got to take a lift. __ From re -

- a - li - ty I just can't drift. __ That's why __ I'm stay-in' with this riff.

Take it ea - sy. __ Lord, now take it
Got __ to

ea - sy. Take it ea - sy. __

9
GET UP, STAND UP

WORDS & MUSIC BY BOB MARLEY & PETER TOSH

Moderately slow Reggae

Get up,   stand up,   stand up   for___ your right.
get up,   stand up,   stand up   for___ your right.
get up,   stand up,   stand up   for___ your right.

Get up,   stand up,   stand up   for___ your right.
Get up,   stand up,   don't give up___ the fight.
Get up,   stand up,   don't give up___ the fight.

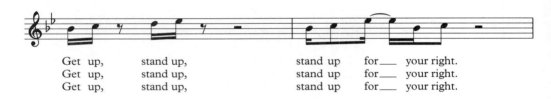

Get up,   stand up,   stand up   for___ your right.
Get up,   stand up,   stand up   for___ your right.
Get up,   stand up,   stand up   for___ your right.

Get up,   stand up,   don't give up___ the fight.
Get up,   stand up,   don't give up___ the fight.
Get up,   stand up,   don't give up___ the fight.   We're

Preacher man, don't tell___ me___   hea-ven is un - der the earth.
Most peo - ple think   great God will come from the sky,
sick and tired   of your is-m and skism game. Die and go to hea-ven in Je-sus' name, Lord.

I know you don't know   what— life is real-ly worth.   Is not all—
take a - way ev-'ry-thing,   and make ev - 'ry-bo-dy feel high.   But
We know when we un - der-stand.   Al-migh-ty God is a   liv-ing man. You can fool

— that glit - ters is gold?—   And half— the sto-ry has ne - ver been told.   So
if you know what life is worth,   you— would look   for yours on earth. And
— some peo - ple some-times, but   you can't fool all the peo-ple all the time.   So

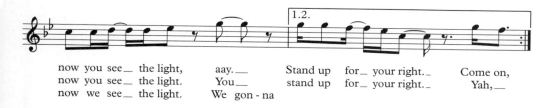

now you see— the light,   aay. —   Stand up   for— your right.—   Come on,
now you see— the light.   You—   stand up   for— your right.—   Yah, —
now we see— the light.   We gon - na

stand up   for— our right.   So— you'd bet-ter   get up,   stand up,

repeat to fade

stand up for your right.   Get up,   stand up,   don't give up— the fight.

GUAVA JELLY

WORDS & MUSIC BY BOB MARLEY

Moderate Reggae

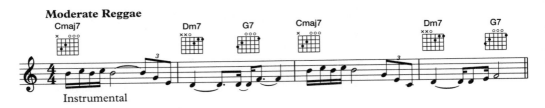

Instrumental

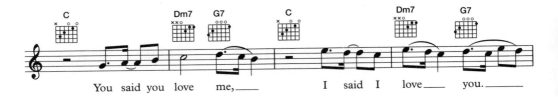

You said you love me, ___ I said I love ___ you. ___

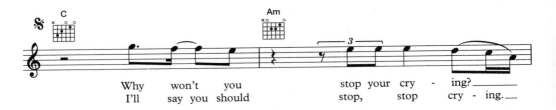

Why won't you ___ stop your cry - ing? ___
I'll say you should ___ stop, stop cry - ing. ___

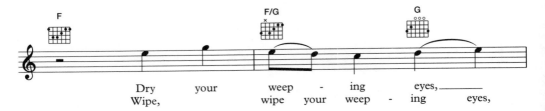

Dry your weep - ing eyes, ___
Wipe, wipe your weep - ing eyes,

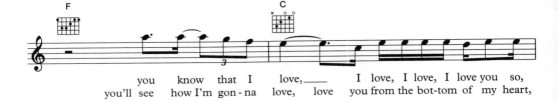

you know that I love, ___ I love, I love, I love you so,
you'll see how I'm gon - na love, love you from the bot-tom of my heart,

da - da - dam da - da - dam - sel. ___ Here I ___ am. ___ Me said, 'Come

11
I SHOT THE SHERIFF

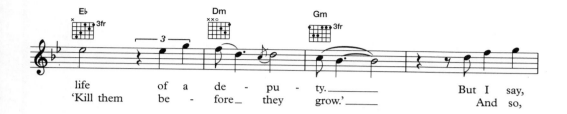

life of a de - pu - ty. ___ But I say,
'Kill them be - fore_ they grow.' ___ And so,

Instrumental

oh, now, now.

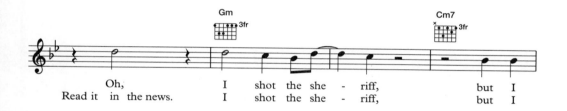

Oh, I shot the she - riff, but I
Read it in the news. I shot the she - riff, but I

swear it was in self de - fence. Ooh, ooh,_ ooh.
swear it was in self de - fence. Ooh, ooh_ ooh.

I said, I shot the she - riff, oh Lord, and they
I shot the she - riff, but I

say it is a ca - pi - tal of - fence._ Ohh, ooh,_ ooh.
swear it was in self de - fence.

Hear this.

Free - dom came my way one
-flex - es had the bet - ter of

day and I start - ed out of town,
me. And what is to be must____

__ yeah! All of a sud-den I saw
be.____ Ev - 'ry day the buck-et a - go a

She-riff John Brown aim - in' to shoot me down.
well, one day the bot - tom ago drop out.

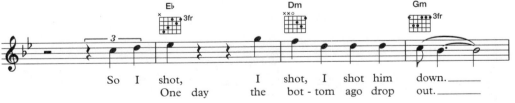

So I shot, I shot, I shot him down.____
One day the bot - tom ago drop out.____

And I say,
I say,

Instrumental

to Coda ⊕

12

I'M HURTING INSIDE

WORDS & MUSIC BY BOB MARLEY
© COPYRIGHT 1972 CAYMAN MUSIC INCORPORATED, USA.
BLUE MOUNTAIN MUSIC LIMITED, 47 BRITISH GROVE, LONDON W4.
ALL RIGHTS RESERVED. INTERNATIONAL COPYRIGHT SECURED.

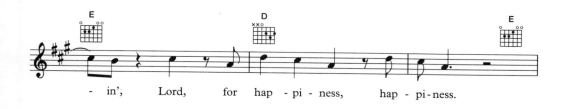

- in';   Lord,   for   hap - pi - ness,   hap - pi - ness.

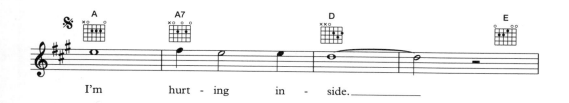

I'm   hurt - ing   in - side._____

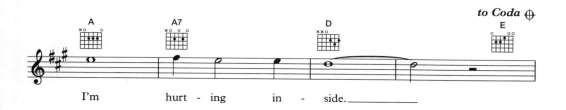

I'm   hurt - ing   in - side._____

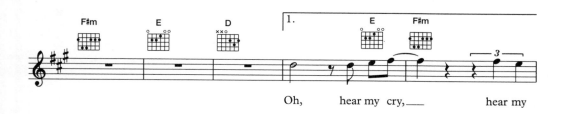

Oh,   hear my cry,___   hear my

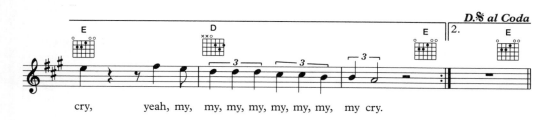

cry,   yeah, my,   my, my, my, my, my, my,   my cry.

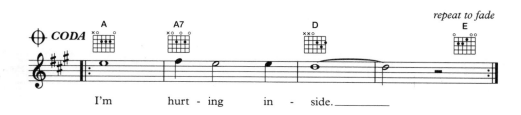

I'm   hurt - ing   in - side._____

13
I'M STILL WAITING

WORDS & MUSIC BY BOB MARLEY
© COPYRIGHT 1968 CAYMAN MUSIC INCORPORATED, USA.
BLUE MOUNTAIN MUSIC LIMITED, 47 BRITISH GROVE, LONDON W4.
ALL RIGHTS RESERVED. INTERNATIONAL COPYRIGHT SECURED.

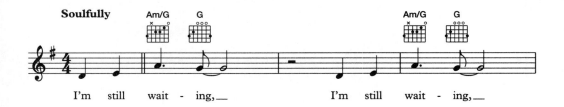

I'm still wait - ing, ___ I'm still wait - ing, ___

I'm still wait - ing, ___ I'm still wait - ing ___ for

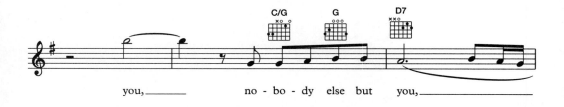

you, ___ no - bo - dy else but you, ___

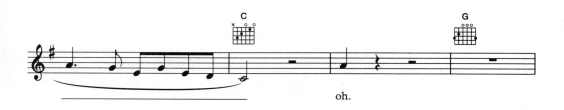

___ oh.

My feet ___ won't keep me up a - ny
Why, girl, ___ oh, ___

IS THIS LOVE?

WORDS & MUSIC BY BOB MARLEY

Moderate Reggae, swing feel

15

IRON LION ZION

WORDS & MUSIC BY BOB MARLEY
© COPYRIGHT 1992 BOB MARLEY MUSIC LIMITED.
BLUE MOUNTAIN MUSIC LIMITED, 47 BRITISH GROVE, LONDON W4.
ALL RIGHTS RESERVED. INTERNATIONAL COPYRIGHT SECURED.

Reggae, swing feel

Well,   I'm on the rock,   and then_
I'm on the run,   but I ain't_
I'm on the run,   but I don't

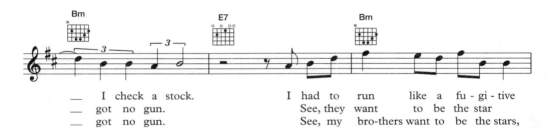

__ I check a stock.   I had to run like a fu - gi - tive
__ got no gun.   See, they want to be the star
__ got no gun.   See, my bro-thers want to be the stars,

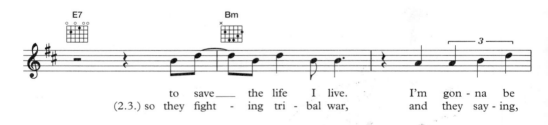

to save__ the life I live.   I'm gon - na be
(2.3.) so they fight - ing tri - bal war,   and they say - ing,

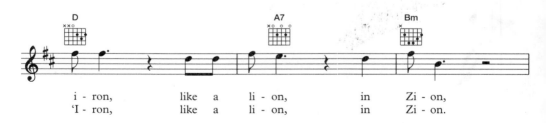

i - ron,   like a li - on,   in Zi - on,
'I - ron,   like a li - on,   in Zi - on.

to Coda ⊕

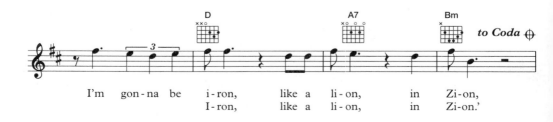

I'm gon-na be i-ron,   like a li - on,   in Zi - on,
I-ron,   like a li - on,   in Zi - on.'

oh yeah.   Li-on,   i-ron,   Zi-on,   li-on,   Zi-on.
I-ron,   li-on,   Zi-on.

I'm on   the rock,

I   check   a   stock.

I   had to   run like   a   fu - gi - tive,_____

just   to, just   to save   the life____   I   live,_____

oh   now.   And   still I'm gonna be   ir - on   like   a

li - on   in   Zi - on.   I'm   gon - na   be

i - ron,   like   a   li - on   in   Zi - on.   What

did you   say?__   I - ron,   li - on,   Zi - on.

CODA

Steal them off of me.   I-ron, li-on, Zi-on.

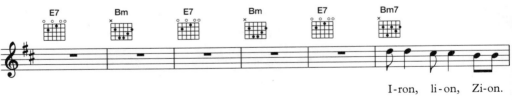

I-ron, li-on,   Zi-on.

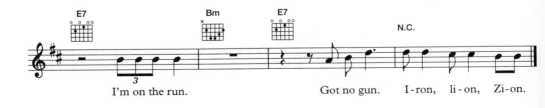

I'm on the run.   Got no gun.   I-ron, li-on, Zi-on.

16
JAMMING

WORDS & MUSIC BY BOB MARLEY
© COPYRIGHT 1977 BOB MARLEY MUSIC LIMITED.
BLUE MOUNTAIN MUSIC LIMITED, 47 BRITISH GROVE, LONDON W4.
ALL RIGHTS RESERVED. INTERNATIONAL COPYRIGHT SECURED.

Moderate Reggae, swing feel

Well, al - right. __ We're jam - min'.
jam - min'.
-wa. We're jam - min'.

I wan - na jam it with you. __ We're
To think that jam-min' was a thing of the past. __ We're
I wan - na jam it with you. __ We're

jam-min', jam - min', and I hope you like jam-min', too.
jam-min', jam - min', and I hope this jam is gon - na last.
jam-min', and jam down, hope you're jam - min' too.

— Ain't no rules, __ ain't no vow, __ we can do
— No bul - let can stop us now, we nei - ther
— Jah knows how much I've tried, the

it a - ny - how. __ I and I will see you through,
beg nor we won't bow. Nei - ther can be bought nor sold. __
truth can - not hide, __ to keep you sa - tis - fied.

17
LICK SAMBA

WORDS & MUSIC BY BOB MARLEY
© COPYRIGHT 1971 BOB MARLEY MUSIC LIMITED.
BLUE MOUNTAIN MUSIC LIMITED, 47 BRITISH GROVE, LONDON W4.
ALL RIGHTS RESERVED. INTERNATIONAL COPYRIGHT SECURED.

18
LIVELY UP YOURSELF

WORDS & MUSIC BY BOB MARLEY

Bright Reggae Shuffle

Oh, live - ly up __ your - self __ and don't be no drag,

live - ly up __ your - self, __ reg-gae is an - oth-er bag.

Live - ly up __ your - self __ and don't say no. __

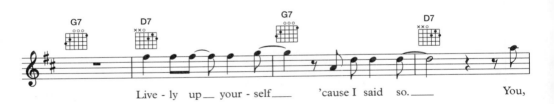

Live - ly up __ your - self __ 'cause I said so. __ You,

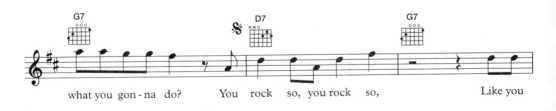

what you gon - na do? You rock so, you rock so, Like you

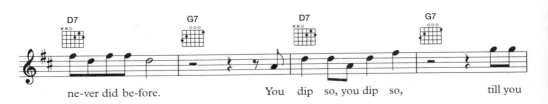

ne - ver did be - fore. You dip so, you dip so, till you

19
MELLOW MOOD

WORDS & MUSIC BY BOB MARLEY

Moderate Reggae

I'll play your fav'r-ite song, dar - lin'. We can rock it all night

long, dar - lin'. 'Cause I've got love, dar - lin',

love, sweet love, dar - lin'. Mel - low mood has
Qui - et as the

got me, so let the mu - sic rock me.
night, please turn off your light.

I'll play your fav'r - ite song, dar - lin'.

We can rock it all night long, dar - lin'.

NATURAL MYSTIC

WORDS & MUSIC BY BOB MARLEY

Moderate Reggae, swing feel

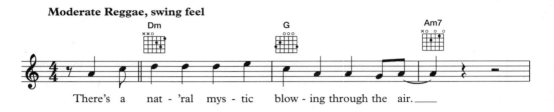

There's a nat - 'ral mys - tic blow - ing through the air.____

If you lis - ten care - ful - ly____ now, you will hear.
and all got to face____ re - a - li - ty

now. This could be the first trum-
Though I try to find the
be the first trum-

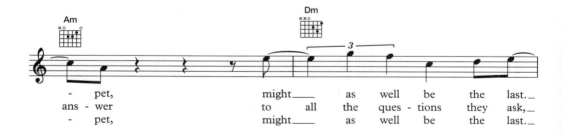

- pet, might____ as well be the last.__
ans - wer to all the ques - tions they ask,__
- pet, might____ as well be the last.__

____ Ma - ny more will have to suf -
____ though I know it's im - pos - si -
____ Ma - ny more will have to suf -

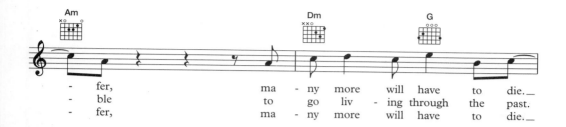

	Am						Dm			G

- fer, ma - ny more will have to die.___
- ble to go liv - ing through the past.
- fer, ma - ny more will have to die.___

Am   Dm   Am

___   Don't__ ask me_____ why.
___   Don't__ tell no_____ lie.
___   Don't__ ask me_____ why.   There's
    There's

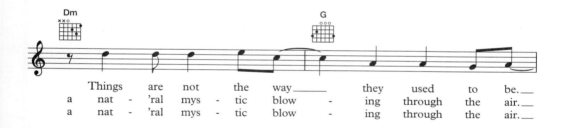

Dm   G

   Things are not the way_____ they used to be.___
a nat - 'ral mys - tic blow - ing through the air.___
a nat - 'ral mys - tic blow - ing through the air.___

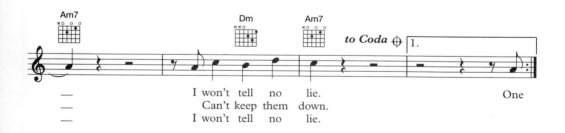

Am7   Dm   Am7   *to Coda* ⊕ |1.

___   I won't tell no lie.
    Can't keep them down.
___   I won't tell no lie.   One

|2.   Dm   G

If you lis - ten care - ful - ly_____ now, you will hear.

Such a nat - 'ral   mys - tic___

blow - ing   through   the   air.

D.$\mathsection$ al Coda   ⊕ **CODA**

This could   If   you   lis - ten   care - ful - ly _

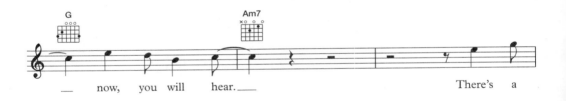

__   now,   you   will   hear.___   There's   a

nat - 'ral   mys - tic   blow - ing through the air.___   Such a   nat - 'ral

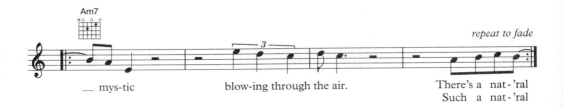

repeat to fade

__ mys-tic   blow-ing through the air.   There's a   nat - 'ral
                                                           Such a   nat - 'ral

NO WOMAN, NO CRY

WORDS & MUSIC BY BOB MARLEY & VINCENT FORD

22
NICE TIME

WORDS & MUSIC BY BOB MARLEY

Moderately

Instrumental

Long time we no have no nice time, doo yoo - dee-dun-doo-yea.

Think a-bout that. Long time we no have no nice time,

doo yoo - dee-dun - doo - yea. Think a-bout that.

This is my heart to rock you stea - dy.

I'll give you love the time you're rea - dy.

This__ lit - tle heart in me just won't let__ me be.__

I'm just to rock you, now. Won't you rock__ with me?__

Long time we no have no nice time,

doo yoo - dee-dun - doo, yea. Think a - bout that.

to Coda ✛

1.

2. *D.S. al Coda*

repeat to fade

✛ *CODA*

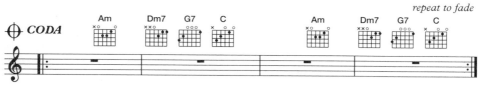

23

ONE LOVE

WORDS & MUSIC BY BOB MARLEY
© COPYRIGHT 1964 CAYMAN MUSIC INCORPORATED, USA.
BLUE MOUNTAIN MUSIC LIMITED, 47 BRITISH GROVE, LONDON W4.

Relaxed Reggae beat

One love, one heart. Let's get to-geth - er and

feel al - right. Hear the chil-dren cry - ing. (One love.) Hear the chil-dren
As it was in the be - gin -ning. (One love.) So shall it be in the
I'm plead-ing to__ man-kind. (One love.) Oh, Lord._____

to Coda ⊕

cry - ing. (One heart.) Say-in',
end._ (One heart.) Al-right, 'Give thanks and praise to the Lord and I will
_____ (One heart.) Whoa.

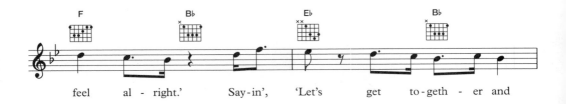

feel al - right.' Say-in', 'Let's get to-geth - er and

feel al - right.' Whoa, whoa, whoa, whoa. Let them all pass all_ their
One more thing. Let's get to-geth - er_ to

24
PLEASE DON'T ROCK MY BOAT

WORDS & MUSIC BY BOB MARLEY
© COPYRIGHT 1972 CAYMAN MUSIC INCORPORATED, USA.
BLUE MOUNTAIN MUSIC LIMITED, 47 BRITISH GROVE, LONDON W4.
ALL RIGHTS RESERVED. INTERNATIONAL COPYRIGHT SECURED.

Moderately slow Reggae

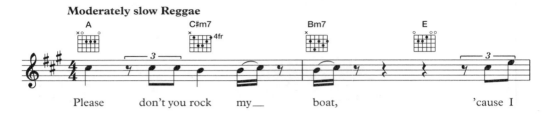

Please   don't you rock   my＿   boat,   'cause I

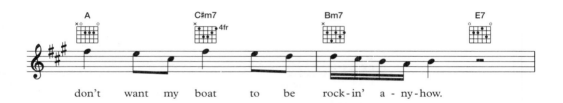

don't   want   my boat   to   be   rock-in'   a - ny-how.

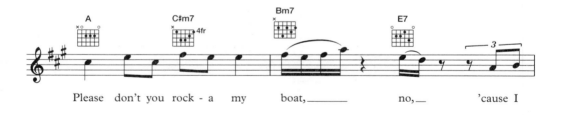

Please   don't you rock - a   my   boat,＿＿   no,＿   'cause I

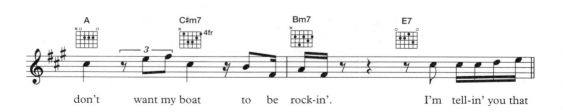

don't   want my boat   to   be rock-in'.   I'm   tellin' you that

oh,   ooh, oh,＿   I like it a-like a - this.   Can you miss?
oh,   ooh, oh,＿   I like it a-like a - this.   Yes I do.

I'm call-in', call-in'. Sa-tis-fy my soul, sa-tis-fy my soul.

Ne-ver, ne - ver, ne-ver give it up now.

We're all in the same boat, rock-in' on the same

rope. We've got to get to - geth - er, lov-ing each

oth - er. And can't you see what I've got for you, yeah.

repeat ad lib. to fade

I'm hap-py, hap-py, hap-py, hap-py, hap-py, hap-py and not ev-en time to be blue yeah.

25

REDEMPTION SONG

WORDS & MUSIC BY BOB MARLEY
© COPYRIGHT 1980 BOB MARLEY MUSIC LIMITED.
BLUE MOUNTAIN MUSIC LIMITED, 47 BRITISH GROVE, LONDON W4.

Moderately, folk style

Instrumental

Old

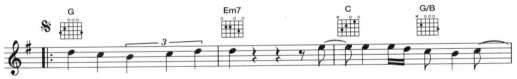

pir - ates, yes, they rob I.   Sold__ I to the mer-chant ships__
-pate your-selves from men-tal slav-'ry, none but our - selves can free our minds.

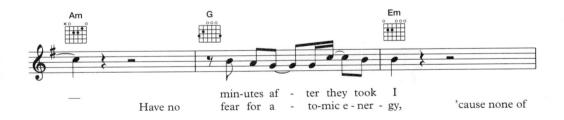

__   min-utes af - ter they took I
Have no   fear for a - to-mic e - ner - gy,   'cause none of

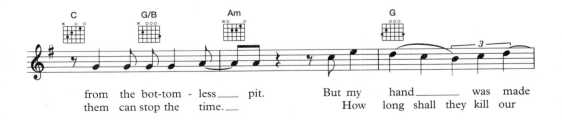

from the bot-tom - less__ pit.   But my hand_____ was made
them can stop the time.__   How long shall they kill our

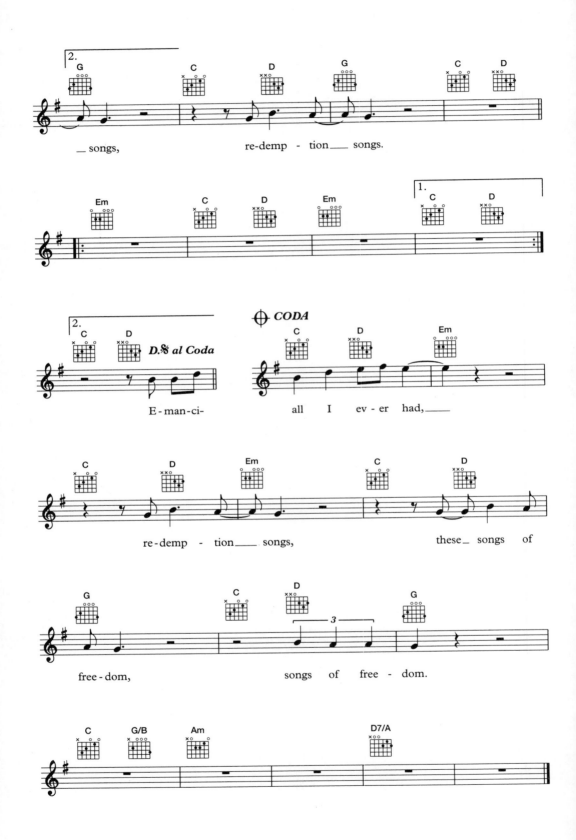

26

SO MUCH TROUBLE IN THE WORLD

WORDS & MUSIC BY BOB MARLEY

Moderate Reggae

sail-ing on their e - go trips,
they're sit-ting on a time bomb,

blast off on their space - ships,
now I know the time has come,

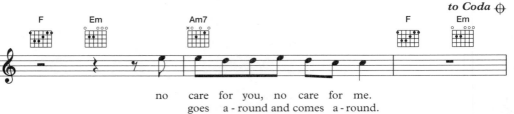

mil - lion miles from re - a - li - ty;
what goes on up is com-ing on down,

to Coda

no care for you, no care for me.
goes a - round and comes a - round.

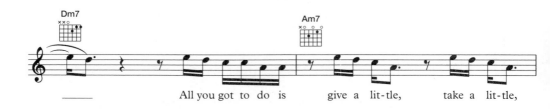

So much trou - ble in the world. ___
So much trou - ble in the world.

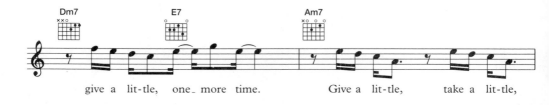

___ All you got to do is give a lit-tle, take a lit-tle,

give a lit-tle, one_ more time. Give a lit-tle, take a lit-tle,

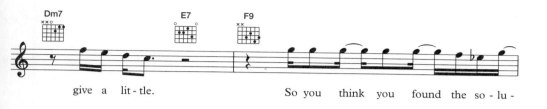

give a lit-tle. So you think you found the so-lu-

-tion, but it's___ just an-oth-er il-lu-

-sion. So be-fore_ you check out this tide,

D.$ al Coda

don't leave an-oth-er cor-ner-stone stand-ing there be-hind.

CODA

So much trou-ble in the world.___

repeat to fade

So much trou-ble in the world.___ There is

SMALL AXE

WORDS & MUSIC BY BOB MARLEY

SOUL REBEL

WORDS & MUSIC BY BOB MARLEY
© COPYRIGHT 1971 BOB MARLEY MUSIC LIMITED.
BLUE MOUNTAIN MUSIC LIMITED, 47 BRITISH GROVE, LONDON W4.
ALL RIGHTS RESERVED. INTERNATIONAL COPYRIGHT SECURED.

Moderate Reggae

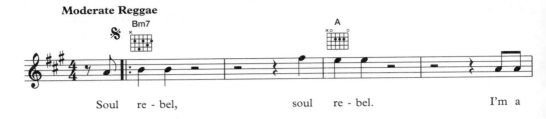

Soul re - bel, soul re - bel. I'm a

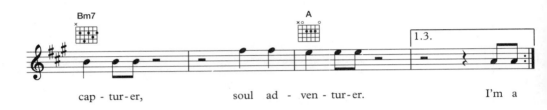

cap - tur - er, soul ad - ven - tur - er. I'm a

See the morn - ing sun, see the morn - ing sun,

on the hill - side. If you're not liv -

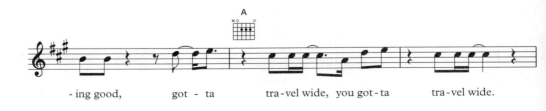

- ing good, got - ta tra - vel wide, you got - ta tra - vel wide.

SUN IS SHINING

WORDS & MUSIC BY BOB MARLEY

rain - bow, _   want you to know   I'm a

rain - bow, too.   So, to the res - cue,   here I

am.   Want you to know just if you can, _ where I

stand,   know, know, know, know, know, know, know, know.

We'll lift our heads and give Jah prai - ses,

we'll lift our heads and give Jah prai - ses, yeah.____

Sun is shin - ing, the wea - ther is sweet.

Make you want to move your danc - ing feet. To the

res - cue, here I am. Want you

to know just if you can__ where I stand, no, no, no, no, where I stand.

repeat to fade

Sun is shin-ing, sun is shin-ing.

30

STIR IT UP

WORDS & MUSIC BY BOB MARLEY
© COPYRIGHT 1972 CAYMAN MUSIC INCORPORATED, USA.
BLUE MOUNTAIN MUSIC LIMITED, 47 BRITISH GROVE, LONDON W4.

Moderate Reggae

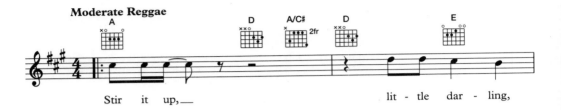

Stir it up, ___ lit - tle dar - ling,

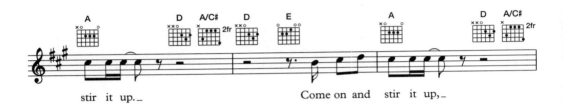

stir it up. ___ Come on and stir it up, ___

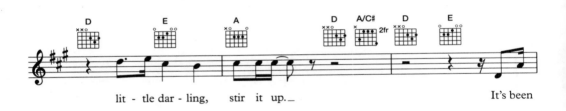

lit - tle dar - ling, stir it up. ___ It's been

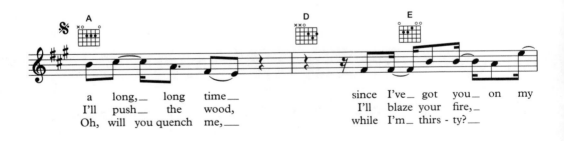

a long, ___ long time ___ since I've ___ got you ___ on my
I'll push ___ the wood, I'll blaze your fire, ___
Oh, will you quench me, ___ while I'm ___ thirs - ty? ___

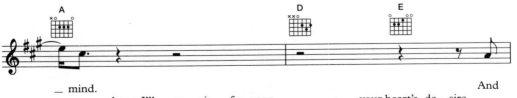

___ mind.
then I'll sa - tis - fy your, your heart's de - sire. And
Or would you cool me down when I'm hot?

now you are___ here, I___ say, it's so clear,___
Said I'll stir it, yeah, ev - 'ry min-ute, yeah.
Your re - ci - pe, dar-ling, is so tas - ty,

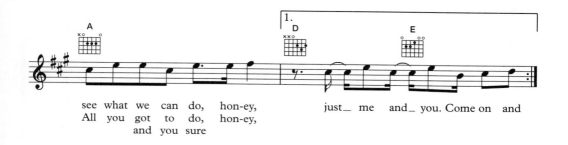

1.

see what we can do, hon-ey, just___ me and___ you. Come on and
All you got to do, hon-ey, and you sure

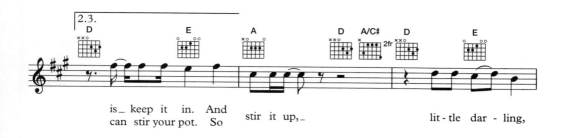

2.3.

is___ keep it in. And
can stir your pot. So stir it up,___ lit - tle dar - ling,

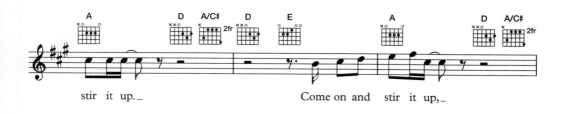

stir it up.___ Come on and stir it up,___

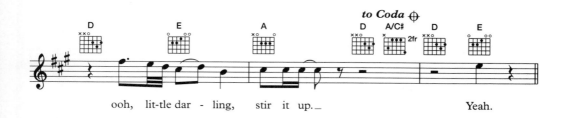

to Coda

ooh, lit-tle dar - ling, stir it up.___ Yeah.

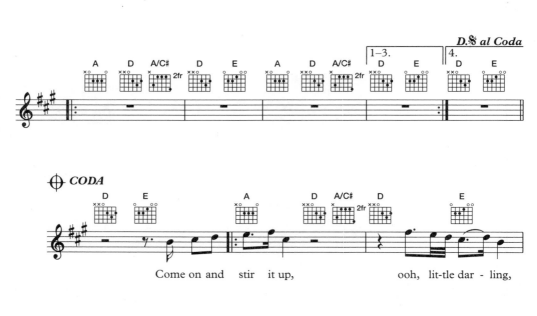

⊕ *CODA*

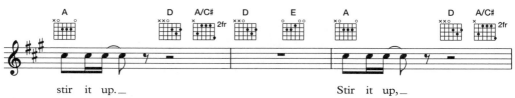

Come on and   stir   it up,   ooh, lit-tle dar - ling,

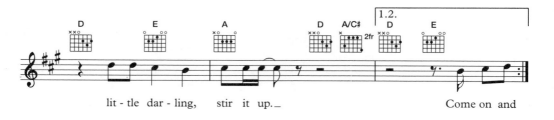

stir   it   up. __   Stir   it   up, __

lit - tle dar - ling,   stir it up. __   Come on and

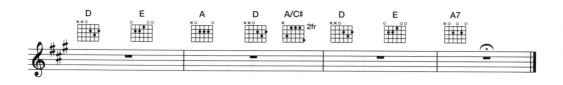

31

THANK YOU LORD

WORDS & MUSIC BY BOB MARLEY
© COPYRIGHT 1972 CAYMAN MUSIC INCORPORATED, USA.
BLUE MOUNTAIN MUSIC LIMITED, 47 BRITISH GROVE, LONDON W4.
ALL RIGHTS RESERVED. INTERNATIONAL COPYRIGHT SECURED.

Say I'm___ in no_____ com - pe -
Said I_____ can't find_____ the ex - pla -

- ti - tion, Lord___ have mer - cy, but I
- na - tion, to prove

made my de - ci - sion. You can
my ap - pre - ci - a - tion. Lord, in

keep your o - pin - ion.___ I'm just
my sim - ple way,___ yes, I am a - com-in', com-in',

call - ing on the wise man's com - mun - ion.___
com-in', com-in'. I love to pray._____

Thank you, Lord, for what you've done for me. Ev - 'ry

32

THREE LITTLE BIRDS

WORDS & MUSIC BY BOB MARLEY
© COPYRIGHT 1977 BOB MARLEY MUSIC LIMITED.
BLUE MOUNTAIN MUSIC LIMITED, 47 BRITISH GROVE, LONDON W4.
ALL RIGHTS RESERVED. INTERNATIONAL COPYRIGHT SECURED.

Moderate slow Reaggae

Instrumental

Don't

wor - ry   a - bout_ a thing,_   'cause

ev-'ry lit-tle thing   gon-na be al - right._   Sing-in', 'Don't

wor - ry   a - bout_ a thing,_   'cause

ev-'ry lit-tle thing   gon-na be al - right'._   Rise up this

WAITING IN VAIN

WORDS & MUSIC BY BOB MARLEY

Moderately slow Reggae

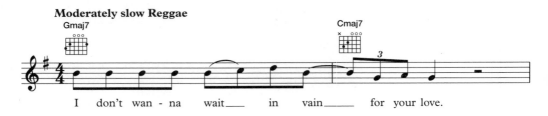

I don't wan - na wait___ in vain_____ for your love.

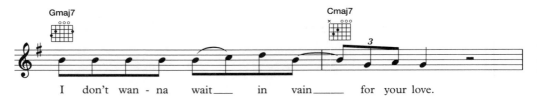

I don't wan - na wait___ in vain_____ for your love.

From the ve - ry first time I blessed my eyes on you,_ girl,
it's been three years since I'm knock - in' on your door,

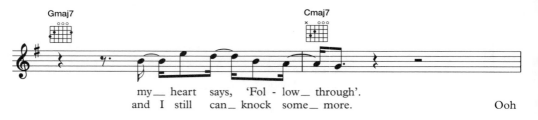

my__ heart says, 'Fol - low__ through'.
and I still can_ knock some_ more.

Ooh

— girl, ooh_ girl, is it fea - si - ble,_ I wan - na know now,
But I know now that I'm way down on your line,

but the wait - ing feel is fine. ___
for I to knock some more?

Ya__ see,

So don't treat me— like a pup-pet on a string,
in life— I know there is lots of grief,

'cause I know how to do my thing.
but your love is my re - lief.

Don't talk— to me— as if you think I'm dumb,
Tears in my eyes burn,— tears in my eyes burn while I'm

I wan - na know when you're gon - na come.—
wai - ting while I'm wait - ing for my turn.— See,

I don't wan - na wait— in vain— for your love.

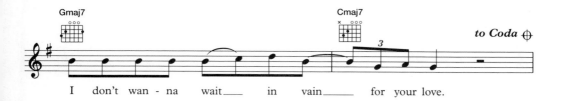

to Coda ⊕

I don't wan - na wait— in vain— for your love.

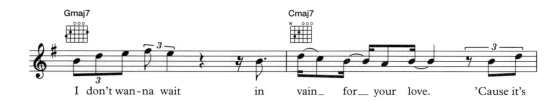

I don't wan-na wait in vain_ for_ your love. 'Cause it's

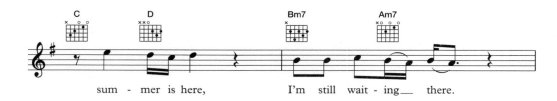

sum - mer is here, I'm still wait-ing_ there.

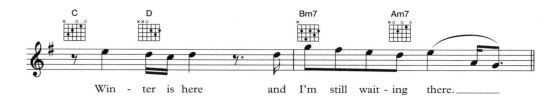

Win - ter is here and I'm still wait-ing there._____

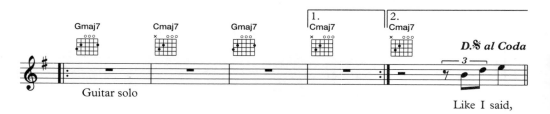

Guitar solo

Like I said,

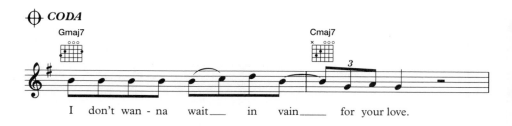

I don't wan - na wait_ in vain_____ for your love.

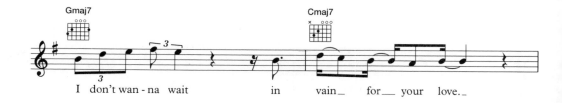

I don't wan - na wait in vain_ for_ your love._

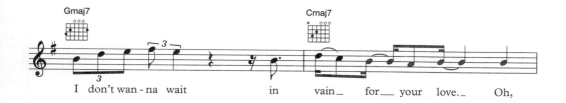

Gmaj7   Cmaj7

I don't wan - na wait   in vain_ for_ your love._   Oh,

Gmaj7

I don't wan - na,   I don't wan - na,   I don't wan - na,   I don't wan - na,

Cmaj7

I don't wan - na wait in   vain.___   No,

Gmaj7

I don't wan - na,   I don't wan - na,   I don't wan - na,   I don't wan - na,

Cmaj7

I don't wan - na wait in   vain.___   It's   your

Gmaj7   Cmaj7   *repeat to fade*

love that I'm wait-ing on.   It's my love that you're run-ning from.   It's your

WHO THE CAP FIT

WORDS & MUSIC BY ASTON BARRETT & CARLTON BARRETT
© COPYRIGHT 1976 RITA MARLEY MUSIC DIVISION & BOB MARLEY MUSIC LIMITED.
BLUE MOUNTAIN MUSIC LIMITED, 47 BRITISH GROVE, LONDON W4.
ALL RIGHTS RESERVED. INTERNATIONAL COPYRIGHT SECURED.

Moderate Reggae, swing feel

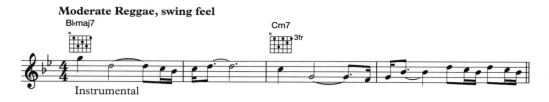

Instrumental

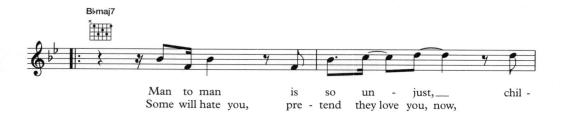

Man to man   is so un - just,___   chil -
Some will hate you,   pre - tend they love you, now,

- dren,   you don't know   who   to trust.
then,   be - hind they___ try to e - li - mi - nate   you.___

Your worst   e - ne - my could be   your___ best friend,
But who Jah bless,   no___ one curse,

and your best   friend your   worst   e - ne - my.
thank   God,   we're   past the worse.

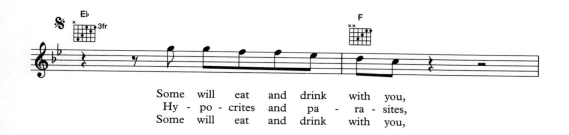

Some will eat and drink with you,
Hy - po - crites and pa - ra - sites,
Some will eat and drink with you,

then be - hind them_ su - su 'pon you.
will come up and_ take a bite.
then be - hind them_ su - su 'pon you.

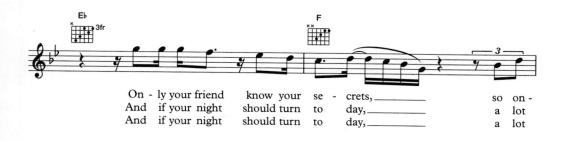

On - ly your friend know your se - crets,_____ so on -
And if your night should turn to day,_____ a lot
And if your night should turn to day,_____ a lot

- ly he could re - veal it.
of peo - ple would run a - way. And who the
of peo - ple would run a - way.

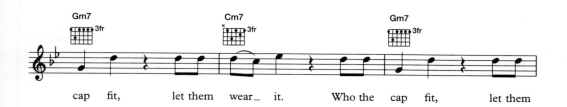

cap fit, let them wear_ it. Who the cap fit, let them

WHY SHOULD I?

WORDS & MUSIC BY BOB MARLEY

should I＿ bend down my＿ head and cry?＿＿＿＿ No rea-son why.

Why should I＿ bend down my＿ head and cry?
(got to move),

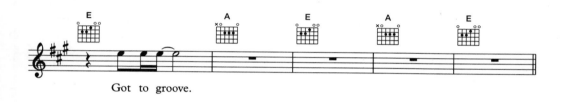

Got to groove.

Got to get＿ what I want. Got to get＿ it. Got to get
＿ it.

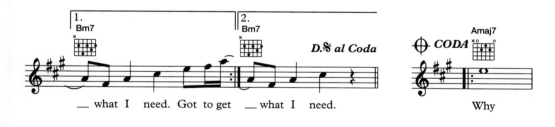

＿ what I need. Got to get ＿ what I need. Why

repeat to fade

should I＿ bend down my＿ head and cry?＿＿＿＿